MY BOOK OF
Farm Noises

This book belongs to:

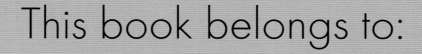

Illustrated by **Kasia Nowowiejska**

Cockerel starts the day with a

COCK-A-DOODL DO

ow joins in with a rumbling

MOO!

OINK

says Pig,

from a very muddy puddle.

WOOF

says Dog,

giving Puppy a cuddle.

B

LEAT
says Goat and
BAA
says Sheep.

Hen ga

CL

s

UCK,

and Chick goes

CHEEP.

CHUG!

goes Tractor –
have you heard?

Frog says "CROAK to Ladybird!

Duck say

QUA

and Hor

NEI

Everyone

Zzz

goes

ZZZZ

at the end of the day!